Grandma Bendy

by Izy Penguin

Our grandma isn't like other grandmas.

She is very bendy!

She has twisty arms,
and loopy legs.

10, 9, 8, 7, 6, 5, 4, 3, 2, 1

This means she is very good

at hide and seek!

But long ago, Grandma Bendy
was very, very bad.

She was a burglar!

Grandma Bendy was a brilliant burglar!
She twisted her way into houses and got
into very small spaces.

Then one day she got home and
found out that she had been burgled!

This made her feel very sad.

It was horrible to be burgled!

She felt so ashamed of her crimes

that she went to the police.

She told them all about the bad
things she had done.

She felt better, but then...

... the police put her in prison!

Many, many years later,

Grandma Bendy was set free.

She did not want to be bendy any
more, in case she got locked up again.

But then, one day, she saw someone who was locked out of their house.

Grandma Bendy knew how to get into houses!

She used her bendy arms
and legs to open the door.

Grandma Bendy was happy.

She started using her bendy arms and legs to help people!

Now everyone loves Grandma Bendy
and her bendy arms and legs!

That is why Grandma Bendy

is the best grandma around!

Quiz

1. Why is the children's Grandma not like any other Grandma?
a) She wears colourful jumpers
b) She is incredibly bendy
c) She does not like knitting

2. Who does Grandma Bendy go to after she is burgled?
a) The police
b) The firemen
c) The doctor

3. Where did Grandma Bendy stay for many years?
a) In a hotel
b) In prison
c) On an island

4. How does Grandma Bendy help her neighbour?
a) She unlocks her door
b) She cooks her a meal
c) She takes her shopping

5. What does Grandma Bendy now use her bendiness for?
a) To burgle people
b) To bake cakes
c) To help people

Turn over for answers

- Pink
- Red (End of Yr R)
- Yellow
- Blue
- Green
- Orange
- Turquoise (End of Yr 1)
- Purple
- Gold
- White (End of Yr 2)
- Lime

Book Bands for Guided Reading

The Institute of Education book banding system is made up of twelve colours, which reflect the level of reading difficulty. The bands are assigned by taking into account the content, the language style, the layout and phonics.

Children learn at different speeds but the colour chart shows the levels of progression with the national expectation shown in brackets. To learn more visit the IoE website: www.ioe.ac.uk.

Maverick early readers have been adapted from the original picture books so that children can make the essential transition from listener to reader. All of these books have been book banded for guided reading to the industry standard and edited by a leading educational consultant.

Quiz Answers: 1b, 2a, 3b, 4a, 5c